KNOWING JESUS

KNOWING JESUS
Discover the man
who is God
Tricia Marnham

INTER-VARSITY PRESS

INTER-VARSITY PRESS
38 De Montfort Street, Leicester LE1 7GP, England

Unless otherwise stated, Scripture quotations in this publication are from the Holy Bible, New International Version. Copyright © 1973, 1978, 1984 International Bible Society. Published in Great Britain by Hodder & Stoughton Ltd.

First published 1990

British Library Cataloguing in Publication Data
Marnham, Tricia
   Knowing Jesus.
   1. Jesus Christ
   I. Title
   232

ISBN 0-85110-681-1

Set in Linotron Clearface and Univers

Typeset in Great Britain by
Parker Typesetting Service, Leicester

Printed in Great Britain by
Cox & Wyman Ltd, Reading

Inter-Varsity Press is the book-publishing division of the Universities and Colleges Christian Fellowship (formerly the Inter-Varsity Fellowship), a student movement linking Christian Unions in universities and colleges throughout the United Kingdom and the Republic of Ireland, and a member movement of the International Fellowship of Evangelical Students. For information about local and national activities write to UCCF, 38 De Montfort Street, Leicester LE1 7GP.

CONTENTS

How to use this book 7

1. How well do you know Jesus? 11
2. Jesus – fully human 21
3. Jesus – fully God 29
4. The resurrection 37
5. Born to be king 45
6. Jesus and the Old Testament 53
7. Jesus' teaching: (1) God and us 59
8. Jesus' teaching: (2) The kingdom 65
9. The cross 71
10. Jesus – our goal 79

ACKNOWLEDGMENTS

Many people have helped in the writing of this book: among them, Clive Lawless gave invaluable advice not only on content but on concept; David Field as theological consultant added countless wise and constructive comments; the editorial staff of IVP guided me with gracious forbearance through the sometimes painful process of writing and re-writing; Sue Bruce, Joyce Dunning and Doreen Lynas bore the burden of typing the manuscript in its several drafts; Georgine Whitfield also assisted with last-minute typing; and finally my husband Charles lent constant affirmation and encouragement. I gratefully dedicate this book to him.

HOW TO USE THIS BOOK

Aim

This workbook aims to help those who are relatively new to the Christian faith to deepen their relationship with Jesus. It will also help those who have been Christians for some time but who know that their discipleship needs to be more sharply focused on the person of Jesus.

The right approach

You will gain most from *Knowing Jesus* if you see it as you would an evening class. Evening classes are increasingly popular: those who are keen to acquire a new skill or take up a particular subject make a conscious decision to set time aside each week and they invest as much energy as they can in their chosen subject.

The workbook is divided into ten separate studies, each of which will take between one and a half and two hours to complete. As with an evening class, the best approach would be to set aside two hours once a week for ten weeks. Do not attempt to do more than one study per week or you will find the work tedious and you will be unable to absorb all that there will be for you to learn.

Unlike some classes, this workbook is not designed to give you theories: the idea is that as you work through the Bible passages set out in each study, you will hear what Jesus has to say about different areas of your life and allow him to change that which is wrong or even that which is good for whatever he considers the best for you and for his purposes.

Alone or with others

The course is designed primarily for individual use, but it could be adapted easily for groups if each study is first completed and then the group, at their meeting, discuss findings and share their responses to the review exercise. Indeed, it could help you keep going if you agree with one or two friends to follow the course together in this way.

Principles

The course is based on three learning principles:

■ First, the value of *writing down* your findings, as an aid to clarifying what you discover and to remembering lessons you have learned. Your notebook will eventually become a record of all that God has said to you through the course.

■ Second, the value of *revising* what you learn, hence the use of a review exercise at the end of each study. Use the following formula each time:

The review exercise
Look back over the study and write answers to these questions in your notebook:

1. What has God been saying to me?
   (Stick to the one or two points that have struck you most forcibly.)
2. What action, if any, should I take?
3. Now pray over what you have noted and ask God's help to remember what he has said and to take any necessary action.

■ Third, the necessity of *applying* what you have learned to your own life. It is the neglect of this step that often leaves people dissatisfied with Bible study. Application and prayer are included therefore as a vital part of the review exercise.

Materials

You will need a notebook or loose-leaf file, a ruler and a Bible, preferably one with cross references. The New International Version is used for all Scripture quotations except where otherwise stated.

Note: Where Bible references are in brackets, it is not essential to look them up.

Abbreviations

IBD   *The Illustrated Bible Dictionary*, 3 volumes (IVP, 1980)
NIV   The New International Version
RSV   The Revised Standard Version

And finally . . .

Enjoy yourself!

HOW WELL DO YOU KNOW JESUS?

1. JESUS AS OTHERS SEE HIM

1.1 Some common misconceptions

Have you ever played 'Chinese Whispers'? A group of players sits in a row. The first person whispers something to his neighbour who in turn whispers what he has heard to his neighbour and so on down the line until the last person says aloud what *he* has heard — usually with hilarious results since he has a totally garbled version of the original statement.

In a similar way, many people have picked up impressions and 'whispers' about Jesus, and the final picture they have is a caricature of the truth. Sometimes he is seen as a tragic political hero, sometimes as a mild and inoffensive teacher; there are Christians who add to the confusion by portraying Jesus rather like a tissue, mopping up tears, meeting whatever 'need' people may have. The common opinion seems to be that you can take this Jesus or leave him, and if you are reasonably self-sufficient, you leave him.

1.2 The view of a translator of the Gospels

In his book *Ring of Truth*, J. B. Phillips describes how, as he translated the Gospels, a very different picture emerged:

> *This man could be moved with compassion and could be very gentle but I could find no trace of the 'Gentle-Jesus-meek-and-mild'. He was quite terrifyingly tough, not in a Bulldog Drummond James Bond sort of way, but in the sheer strength of a unified and utterly dedicated personality. ... I began to see now why the religious Establishment of those days wanted to get rid of him at all costs. He was sudden death to pride, pomposity and pretence.*
>
> J. B. Phillips, *Ring of Truth* (Hodder, 1970), p. 64

Jesus was no sentimental do-gooder but someone whose authority and transforming power were acknowledged by a powerful Roman centurion[1] and even by a hard-bitten tax collector.[2] Such people were not fooled. They recognized, as did all those who met him, that *the one thing you cannot do with Jesus Christ is to ignore him.*

1.3 What does Jesus mean to you?

Before going any further, draw a chart on the first page of your notebook, as set out in the diagram opposite. In the left-hand column write short answers to the questions that follow. Leave the other column blank for now.

■ Describe briefly in your own words the nature of your relationship with Jesus. Is he a close companion, a formal acquaintance, or something in between?
■ What for you are the most important facets of his personality?

[1] Luke 7:1–10.
[2] Luke 19:1–10

12

WHAT JESUS MEANS TO ME	
As I begin this study	As I conclude it

2. THE FACTS THAT LUKE RECORDED

2.1 Close-up

We are now going to look at four passages from Luke's Gospel. Each of them portrays a particular facet of Jesus' character.

JESUS IS . . .

▨ *the source of authority*
READ Luke 7:1–10.

Here we see that it took a Roman soldier whose training was based on authority to understand the force behind any word spoken by Jesus. It has to be the same for us. If Jesus really is God-in-the-flesh, then I have to do what he commands and accept what he says as absolute truth whether or not I like it or find it convenient.

'I can't accept Jesus' claim to be the only way to God' (see John 14:6). In view of the centurion's example, write down your reply to anyone who makes a comment like that.

▨ *full of divine power*
READ Luke 8:40–42, 49–56.

This passage highlights Jesus' divine power. Many other

13

passages show the power Jesus had over nature, disease, evil spirits and even, as here, over death. No situation or person was too difficult for him.

Write out Philippians 4:13. Jot down any situation you may be facing in which you feel powerless. Bring it to Jesus now and ask for his strength.

■ *radical*
READ Luke 11:42–46.

Jesus was never afraid to speak out against convention. As is clear here, he was particularly harsh on the Pharisees and scribes (lawyers) who had evolved an intricate web of regulations which had lost sight of God's original intentions.

Is there an unwritten code of rules in your group or church, and if so what are they? Are they laid down in Scripture? How should you react if they are not? (You may find it helpful to talk over this question later with an older Christian.)

Write your answers in your notebook.

■ *compassionate*
READ Luke 19:1–10.

Zacchaeus was wealthy but very unpopular. Following Jesus means having compassion for those we find unattractive, including those who are rich in possessions or talents. Write down your answers to the following:

- Jesus saw Zacchaeus as 'lost' – in what sense?
- What different things did showing compassion involve here?
- What action of Jesus was probably the single most important factor leading to Zacchaeus' conversion?
- Compare this with outreach in your church or group. In what ways could you be following Jesus' example more closely?

Ask God to show you who the Zacchaeus might be in your life and start praying for him or her today.

You are now almost half-way through this study. Pause here for a mug of coffee and a ten-minute break!

2.2 Overview

Are you ready for a challenge? and have you got an hour or so to spare? If you have, read on!

One of the best ways to experience the full force of Jesus' personality and to see the effect he had on his contemporaries is to read a Gospel right through, without stopping. That is the challenge now – to read through the whole of Luke's Gospel in one sitting!

Luke's Gospel gives the fullest picture we have of Jesus' life. A fellow worker with the apostle Paul, Luke was a doctor possessed of a keen historical sense, evident in his prologue (Luke 1:1–4) where he sets out the care with which he wrote his account.

The following suggestions will help:

- Skim (*i.e.* read very quickly) through the Gospel, catching the main gist of the narrative, making a mental note of Jesus' priorities, the attitude he had to different people and what he taught.
- Leave till later any phrases or sections that puzzle you.
- Read over the background note on Palestine on page 17 and refer to the map on page 16 as you read the Gospel.

- In your notebook, jot down any event or saying that particularly strikes you as you read.

- Issue this challenge to a friend, and ask him or her to read the Gospel at the same time as you.

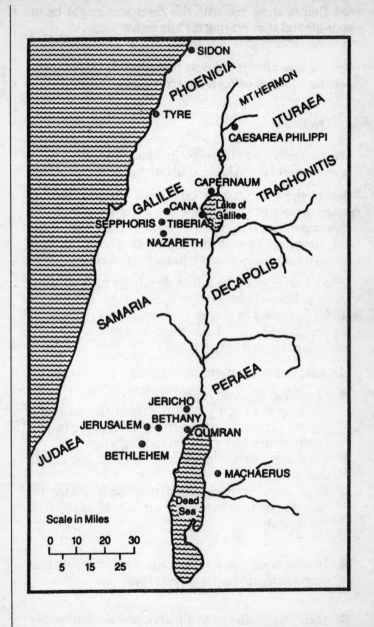

Places prominent in the ministry of Jesus

Before you start, pray that God's Holy Spirit will help you to concentrate, to catch the main gist of the Gospel, and to understand what you read.

If you really would find it too difficult to meet this challenge, don't feel guilty about it! Instead, why not read the Gospel in three parts, but don't leave too long between the episodes. Use the suggestions already listed to help you.

For split reading, the Gospel divides naturally into:
1:1 – 9:50
9:51 – 19:10
19:11 – 24:53

Background note

Palestine, about the size of Wales, was divided into three: to the north, Jesus' home country, Galilee, open to Greek influence and therefore held in suspicion by orthodox Jews; then Samaria, hated by the Jews for its rival temple and priesthood; in the south, the centre of Jewry, Judaea. The Romans had occupied Palestine for sixty years, using local princes like Herod the Great as their satellites. A son of Herod, the regional ruler of Judaea and Samaria, was deposed and replaced by a Roman prefect, Pontius Pilate, in Jesus' time. The Romans were unpopular: they introduced a new kind of harsh slave labour and heavy taxes, administered by dishonest tax-collectors. The main religious parties were the Pharisees, concerned with the intricate application of the religious law; the priestly Sadducees, whose tribunal, the Sanhedrin, had civil and criminal jurisdiction; and the Zealots, political activists, whose mission was to rid the area of Roman rule.

If you have finished your 'chunk' reading, well done! It is not an easy task, but it's well worth the effort.

Read over the brief notes you have made.

NOW HAVE A SHORT BREAK before going on to section 3 and following up your reading of the Gospel.

17

3. HOW DO YOU SEE JESUS NOW?

3.1 Have your views changed?

Turn back to page one of your notebook, and now use the right-hand column of your chart to answer the questions in 1.3 on page 12 of this study.

Compare the two columns. Is there any change in your answers after getting to grips with the whole of a Gospel and looking in detail at aspects of Jesus' personality? Are there ways in which you sense you know Jesus better? Make a note of your conclusions.

3.2 Working at the relationship

A deepening relationship with Jesus is important not only for ourselves but for others. How much more attractive and challenging Christ seems in the person who has an up-to-the-minute account of the reality of his presence. You may have started this study knowing Jesus in a rather formal way; he longs that you should experience more of his dynamic life-giving personality.

In your notebook, write a memo to yourself, setting out how you are going to work at this relationship, perhaps using three or four of the suggestions below. Set specific targets with deadlines; don't just record a few vague hopes!

MEMORANDUM

From:
To: Self
Re: Targets

- Plan to pray once a week with a friend about your devotional life.
- Make an appointment to talk to an older Christian or to your minister, so that you can sort out some of your questions and doubts.
- Jesus may have been convicting you of some sin that is spoiling your relationship with him. Ask him to help you give it up.
- Memorize two key Scripture verses each week of this course. Start with verses which encapsulate two of the four themes on pages 13–14. Then choose two more key verses each week as you do the other studies.
- Write down any difficult patches you may have experienced in the last few months, and consider how Jesus may have used such times to stretch your faith.
- Actively seek to win a friend for Jesus. Write down his or her name, start praying for them, and consider a book you might lend to them or a Christian event to which you could invite them.

Now do the review exercise (see page 8).

STUDY TWO

JESUS – FULLY HUMAN

'A good man!' 'A marvellous teacher!' 'A great prophet!' 'A tragic idealist!' . . .

Whatever reactions you may glean as you ask others what they think of Jesus, it is unlikely that any would doubt he was a man, a real human being.[1]

> *For we do not have a high priest who is unable to sympathise with our weaknesses, but we have one who has been tempted in every way, just as we are – yet was without sin.*   Hebrews 4:15

The Bible highlights two aspects of Jesus' humanity: the first is that in becoming a man, he identified with us, experiencing the different joys, sorrows, difficulties that we face; and the second is that in doing this, he was without sin. Jesus, in other words, lived the perfect human life – and he left for Christians, God's adopted children, the pattern on which to model our lives.

---

[1]This was not always so. See Study Five.

1. 'IN EVERY WAY ...'

Jeşus identified with us in his experience of:

1.1 Family life and work

From your reading of Luke's Gospel in Study One, you will remember that Jesus' early family life seems to have been an ordinary one, except that, at a young age, he possessed a remarkable grasp of his life's work and his relationship to God. We see his mother, brothers and sisters at various times in the Gospels, and it is clear they sometimes found it hard to understand or accept his mission.

Jesus' life was a demanding one – he knew hunger, thirst, tiredness. His personal sorrow for the death of John the Baptist was not allowed to interfere with the needs of those he came to serve. Nor could their more immediate physical needs deflect him from his main goal: to preach the good news and then go to Jerusalem to die for the sins of mankind. He experienced all the emotions: joy (Luke 10:21), compassion (Luke 7:13), anger (Mark 3:5), sorrow at the thought of impending death (Matthew 26:37). He also enjoyed the lighter side of life and we see him at a wedding (John 2) and at various parties and meals; his attendance at these even led to accusations of gluttony and drunkenness.

1.2 Spiritual life

Though from the very beginning Jesus had a unique relationship with the Father (Luke 2:49), there are parallels between his spiritual life and ours.

1.2.1 *Scripture*
Draw a line down the middle of your notebook and head the left-hand column 'Jesus' and the right-hand column 'Me'.

22

READ Luke 4:1–27 and write answers to the following in the left-hand column:

■ In what different ways did Jesus use Scripture?
■ Using the cross references in your own Bible (or borrow a cross-reference edition), list the Old Testament books from which Jesus quotes or to which he refers. What does this tell us about Jesus' knowledge of the Old Testament?

Now in the right-hand column answer:

■ Which of the Old Testament books listed in the left-hand column have you studied?
■ How does your attitude to, and knowledge of, the Old Testament compare to that of Jesus?
■ As a follower of Jesus, is there any action you think he might want you to take?

1.2.2 *Prayer*
Look up Mark 1:32–35; Luke 6:12, 13; 10:17–21.

Under 'Jesus', answer in your notebook:

■ In what circumstances did Jesus pray and at what time of day?

Under 'Me':
■ How does my prayer life match up to this?

1.2.3 *Temptation*
From Luke 4:1–13, write answers to the following under 'Jesus':

■ When was Jesus tempted? (You will have to look back into Luke 3.)
■ Which sins was Satan hoping Jesus would commit?
■ How did Jesus resist?
■ What is the significance of verse 13?

Under 'Me', write down any particular temptation you may be experiencing. How do you think Jesus might help you? Ask him now to do so.

PAUSE HERE – perhaps have a mug of coffee before going on.

1.3 **Suffering**

Suffering runs like a dark thread through the earthly life of Jesus; this should not surprise us. Isaiah prophesied (see Isaiah 53, especially verse 10a) that the Messiah would come as a suffering servant – for him there would be no easy path through life. Isaiah's prophecy was confirmed by Simeon as he held the baby Jesus:

> *This child is destined to cause the falling and rising of many in Israel, and to be a sign that will be spoken against, so that the thoughts of many hearts will be revealed.*   Luke 2:34–35

Look up Matthew 26:36–75 and think yourself into each situation, asking God to give you a fresh picture of what are perhaps familiar incidents.

■ Now write down some of the ways in which Jesus suffered.

People who have experienced much suffering, perhaps through bereavement or some other tragedy, often say that their distress is made worse by friends who, out of embarrassment, avoid them. Maybe their friends lack real compassion, or maybe they just cannot handle another person's grief.

■ From your reading of Luke try to remember the times when Jesus by contrast went out of his way to identify with those who were suffering.

If you have experienced some deep sorrow, you will know that part of the pain is the belief that no-one else knows what you are going through; often you feel alone, and sometimes angry with God for 'letting it happen'.

■ How could the knowledge that Jesus suffered help you? Make a note of your answer.

2. '... YET WITHOUT SIN ...'

Jesus not only identified with us in our everyday existence; he showed us how to live: his was a perfect, sinless life – even his enemies had to concede that (see Study Three).

Why then was Jesus baptized by John (Luke 3:21–22) if John's baptism was a baptism of repentance (Luke 3:3)? The answer must surely be that at the outset of his ministry, Jesus was identifying both with the sinners he came to save and with the message John was preaching, namely, the need for God's people to be pure and renewed. Yet if death was the penalty for sinners (Romans 6:23) why did the sinless Jesus die? The answer (looked at more fully in Study Nine) is that Jesus in his death took the place of those same sinners, as their human representative; thus he made it possible for them one day to be perfected in heaven.

In Romans 5:18, Paul contrasts the two men, Adam and Christ:

> *Then as one man's trespass led to condemnation for all men, so one man's act of righteousness leads to acquittal and life for all men.* (RSV)

25

Questions are often raised about two aspects of Jesus' humanity:

His limited knowledge

In particular this refers to Mark 13:32 where Jesus states he does not know the day or hour of his return. Bruce Milne in *Know the Truth* comments: 'Ignorance, however, does not equal error. . . . It is impossible therefore to think of Jesus as mistaken . . . The Scripture presents a careful balance here; a unique and unclouded awareness of the Father and his will (Luke 2:49) co-exists with a search for further understanding (Luke 2:46).'

His temptations

Since Jesus was sinless, were the temptations as great a struggle for him as they are for us? Bruce Milne replies that those we face are 'filtered' by God (1 Corinthians 10:13) but for Jesus 'the filter was removed . . . as true man he endured the weight and pull of temptation to a degree we shall never experience.'

Bruce Milne, *Know the Truth* (IVP, 1982), pp. 126 and 127

Write out a summary of what you have learned from section 2.

3. RESPONSE

Write out Hebrews 4:15–16 and then meditate on what you have learned of Jesus in this study, responding to him in a time of prayer.

The Bible teaches that, one day, Jesus will return to judge all people. His sufferings as a human qualified him to do this, as is shown in the piece called *The Long Silence*. Read it prayerfully, remembering what you studied in section 1.3 above, and thank him that he was willing to go through all he did . . . for you.

THE LONG SILENCE

At the end of time, billions of people were scattered on a great plain before God's throne.

Most shrank back from the brilliant light before them. But some groups near the front talked heatedly – not with cringing shame, but with belligerence.

'Can God judge us? How can he know about suffering?' snapped a pert young brunette. She ripped open a sleeve to reveal a tattooed number from a Nazi concentration camp. 'We endured terror ... beatings ... torture ... death!'

In another group a Negro boy lowered his collar. 'What about this?' he demanded, showing an ugly rope burn. 'Lynched ... for no crime but being black!'

In another crowd, a pregnant schoolgirl with sullen eyes. 'Why should I suffer?' she murmured. 'It wasn't my fault.'

Far out across the plain there were hundreds of such groups. Each had a complaint against God for the evil and suffering he permitted in his world. How lucky God was to live in heaven where all was sweetness and light, where there was no weeping or fear, no hunger or hatred. What did God know of all that man had been forced to endure in this world? For God leads a pretty sheltered life, they said.

So each of these groups sent forth their leader, chosen because he had suffered the most. A Jew, a Negro, a person from Hiroshima, a horribly deformed arthritic, a thalidomide child. In the centre of the plain they consulted with each other. At last they were ready to present their case. It was rather clever.

Before God could be qualified to be their judge, he must endure what they had endured. Their decision was that God should be sentenced to live on earth – as a man!

'Let him be born a Jew. Let the legitimacy of his birth be doubted. Give him a work so difficult that even his family will think him out of his mind when he tries to do it. Let him be betrayed by his closest

27

friends. Let him face false charges, be tried by a prejudiced jury and convicted by a cowardly judge. Let him be tortured.

'At the last, let him see what it means to be terribly alone. Then let him die. Let him die so that there can be no doubt that he died. Let there be a great host of witnesses to verify it.'

As each leader announced his portion of the sentence, loud murmurs of approval went up from the throng of people assembled.

And when the last had finished pronouncing sentence, there was a long silence. No-one uttered another word. No-one moved. For suddenly all knew that God had already served his sentence.

 Now do the review exercise in your notebook.

STUDY THREE

JESUS – FULLY GOD

1. THE FACTS

Jesus was born as a Jew without any of the privacy, still less the safety, of a fully equipped twentieth-century delivery room. The legitimacy of his birth was in question, and he was brought up with his brothers and sisters in a carpenter's home. He remained relatively unknown till he was thirty. Then, for three years, he lived the life of an itinerant preacher with no home and few possessions, his ministry misunderstood by friends and family. He was betrayed by one of his close followers, condemned on the basis of false charges, tortured and then executed like a common criminal.

But that was not all. After his death there rose a great movement, not based on class or nationality – but on the belief that this man Jesus was God, that he is alive and that any who accept him as Lord are received as new people into God's family.

What led to that belief?

1.1 The claims he made for himself

Divide your notebook into two columns; head the left-hand side 'Direct', and the right-hand side 'Indirect'.

1.1.1 *Direct claims*

For each reference in the list below, first think yourself into that situation, then write on the left-hand side what Jesus was claiming for himself and indicate the reaction to each claim (if the Bible passage tells us).

- Luke 24:27 (if you have time, *cf.* Luke 7:18–23)
- John 10:30–33 (if time, *cf.* John 5:17–18 and 14:7–9)
- John 8:56–59

Note The Jews would have linked Jesus' words in John 8:58 with the incident in Exodus 3:13–14, hence their strong reaction.

The *titles* Jesus either gave or accepted for himself may also be seen as direct claims:

- **The Son of Man** is first pictured in Daniel 7:13–14, coming from heaven at the time of judgment and given an everlasting reign over all creatures. It is the title Jesus used most often for himself and it is frequently associated with judgment (Luke 21:36 and *cf.* Mark 14:61–62), but the title underlines what we considered in Study Two, namely Jesus' identification with, and mission for, humanity.

- **Messiah**. The titles Messiah (from the Hebrew) and Christ (from the Greek) both literally mean 'anointed one'. In the Old Testament the term referred especially to the king (*cf.* 1 Samuel 24:6) but also to prophets and priests. Jews had for many centuries expected a Messiah who would establish God's rule on earth but by the time of Jesus' birth, this expectation had taken on the strongly nationalistic overtones of a political rather than a spiritual figure. Jesus was clearly aware that he was the Messiah yet he was reluctant to claim this openly; his concern was to show that his kingdom was not political ('not of this world') but had universal and eternal significance.

Look up Matthew 16:15–17.

■ ***The Son of God*** was the title that most upset the Jews. In both the Old and New Testaments, it is linked with Messiah. It implies oneness with God, and for the Jews, it was blasphemous. Yet as we have seen, when Peter realized who he was, Jesus, far from denying it, declared how favoured Peter was to have had such a revelation.

Jesus' relationship with the Father was indeed unique, for as John Stott says:

> *to know him was to know God;*
> *to see him was to see God;*
> *to believe in him was to believe in God;*
> *to receive him was to receive God;*
> *to hate him was to hate God;*
> *and to honour him was to honour God.*[1]
>
> John Stott, *Basic Christianity* (IVP, 2nd ed. 1971), p. 26

Write these three titles of Jesus in the left-hand column of your notebook.

1.1.2 **Indirect claims**
Here Jesus assumed for himself attributes or actions that could only belong to God.

For each reference below, write in the right-hand column what Jesus was doing. E.g. for John 9:35–38, you could write: He allowed others to worship him (thus implying he was divine).

■ Luke 5:17–26
■ John 9:35–38
■ John 10:28
■ Matthew 5: 27–30

Look carefully over what you have noted in both

[1]John 8:19; 14:7; 12:45; 14:9; 12:44; 14:1; Mark 9:37; John 15:23; 5:23.

columns and write an answer beneath them to the following question:

■ If Jesus was not God, how would you describe a man who made such claims and spoke in such a way?

1.2 The evidence from his life

Jesus did not just make staggering claims for himself; but as those who have looked into it have discovered, his life – the way he lived and what he did – was entirely consistent with these claims.

In your notebook, put the heading *Evidence* and then write a paragraph outlining the case you would make to show Jesus was divine, using material from the following references:

■ Mark 6:1–3
■ 1 John 3:5; Luke 23:13–15
■ Luke 4:33–37, 38–39; 7:11–17
   In each instance, note the standpoint of the people involved and who it is that comments about Jesus.

The fact of the resurrection is crucial to the argument. The evidence for this is examined in the next study. Jesus constantly prophesied that he would die and on the third day rise again, though his disciples failed to understand this. If he did not rise, then clearly his claims to be divine were meaningless.

TAKE A BREAK HERE!

1.3 Only one conclusion

A man who spoke with authority, unlike any other man; a man who had power over disease, nature, evil spirits, death; a man who lived a perfect life and who finally rose from the grave. Could anyone else but the God of all the earth fit this description?

32

Now look again at your answer to the question in 1.1.2 above and consider the following comment which encapsulates the thinking behind this study:

> *I am trying here to prevent anyone saying the really foolish thing that people often say about Him: 'I'm ready to accept Jesus as a great moral teacher but I don't accept His claim to be God.' That is the one thing we must not say. A man who was merely a man and said the sort of thing Jesus said would not be a great moral teacher. He would either be a lunatic – on a level with the man who says he is a poached egg – or else he would be the Devil of Hell. You must make your choice. Either this man was, and is, the Son of God: or else a madman or something worse. You can shut Him up for a fool, you can spit at Him and kill Him as a demon; or you can fall at His feet and call Him Lord and God. But let us not come with any patronising nonsense about His being a great human teacher. He has not left that open to us. He did not intend to.*   C. S. Lewis, *Mere Christianity* (Fontana, 1970), p. 52

1.4 Two other important matters

■ *Virgin birth*

The narratives state that Jesus was born of a virgin, but it is important to note that the virgin birth is never used in Scripture to demonstrate Jesus' deity or Messiahship in the same way that his resurrection is. On the other hand, if Jesus is God, then the fact of a virgin birth will not surprise us. This event highlights the fact that Jesus was the Son of God and that his coming heralded a new start for mankind (Luke 1:35). There is no hint that Mary is without sin.

■ *Miracles*

If one takes a miracle as 'an interference with Nature by supernatural power',[2] and if Jesus was God, then it is quite logical for him to have performed miracles. There

[2] C. S. Lewis, *Miracles* (Fontana, 1960), p. 9.

is no need to explain them away as some have tried to do. Jesus actually refused to perform miracles just to prove who he was (Matthew 16:1–4) and he was anxious not to publicize his powers. He used them to alleviate suffering or meet some other need. But Scripture allows us to see the miracles as pointers to his identity. John indeed in his Gospel calls them 'signs'.

1.5 How do others regard Jesus?

Varying beliefs about Jesus are held by other sects and religions, for example:

Jehovah's Witnesses
Christ is a secondary god, inferior to the one true God, Jehovah. Though he pre-existed, he is not eternal. Instead of being incarnate, the life force of the Son was transferred to Mary and Jesus was born man.

Moonies
Jesus was a man, but sinless; he may well be called God but he is not God himself. His death was never part of God's plan and, as he died, God gave his body to Satan as a ransom for humans – so their souls can be freed but not their bodies.

Mormons
Though acknowledged as God's son, he (like his Father) differs from human beings only in the degree to which he has progressed. He is not unique – just more highly evolved than we are.

Muslims
Jesus was the Messiah, born of a virgin, a miracle-worker and one of the greatest prophets. He denied he was divine. Orthodox Muslims believe he was not crucified – someone else was, by mistake.

2. THE IMPLICATIONS OF JESUS BEING FULLY GOD

2.1 It answers the question, 'How do I know God exists?'

We can argue for the existence of God by saying that someone must be behind the intricate universe in which we live; that someone greater than us must be behind human will and intellect. But ultimately the only way we can know that God exists is if he reveals himself personally and historically so that we can touch and see and hear him ourselves (1 John 1:1–2).

2.2 It answers the question 'What is God like?'

If Jesus is God-in-the-flesh, then in seeing him we see the Father. See also Study Seven.

2.3 It means I must submit to the authority of Jesus

Thomas realized this (John 20:28). To say Jesus is Saviour without implying he is also your Lord must mean you have never realized who he is. Yet many of us only pay lip service to the lordship of Christ.

Stop and consider. Are there areas in your life in which you are saying 'no' to Christ's lordship (something, incidentally, which it is illogical to do if Jesus really is Lord of your life)? Are you perhaps:

- refusing to accept part of his teaching, *e.g.* about his being the only way to God?
- refusing to accept his analysis of human nature?
- refusing to accept his attitude to the Old Testament?
- refusing to accept something else he wants for you?

Write down your answers.

 Now do the review exercise in your notebook.

For further reading

R. T. France, *Jesus the Radical* (IVP, 1989), chapter 5.
Alister McGrath, *Explaining Your Faith* (IVP, 1988), pp.
32–45.

STUDY FOUR

THE RESURRECTION

1. A DISCUSSION WITH AN AGNOSTIC

'Christianity? I honestly can't believe all that fairy-tale nonsense about miracles and people rising from the dead. I suppose I'm an agnostic.'

'Really? Well, how do you explain away all the evidence then?'

This kind of reply often stops such people in their tracks. No-one has ever talked to them about Christianity in terms of evidence – hard, objective, historical facts. Facts like the wildfire spread of Christianity – within sixty years of the death of its founder, the gospel had spread from as far as what we call Iraq and Iran in the East to France and Spain in the West. Facts like the transformation of a nervous bunch of disheartened individuals into the fearless band who caused such upset in the Roman empire with the simple message 'Christ is risen'.

What exactly do Christians believe about the resurrection? Consider the statements made by Paul in a letter probably written no later than thirty years after the death of Christ:

For what I received I passed on to you as of first importance: that Christ died for our sins according to the Scriptures, that he was buried, that he was raised on the third day according to the Scriptures ... After that, he appeared to more than five hundred of the brothers at the same time, most of whom are still living, though some have fallen asleep ...

And if Christ has not been raised, your faith is futile; you are still in your sins ... If only for this life we have hope in Christ, we are to be pitied more than all men.   1 Corinthians 15:3–4, 6, 17, 19

Christianity is based on historical events and it stands or falls on whether the resurrection actually took place.[1] Many people since Paul have realized that if the resurrection did not happen, Christianity is finished. In the 1930s, Frank Morison, a journalist and a Communist, set out to write a book disproving the resurrection; yet after careful sifting of the evidence, he ended up writing a book *Who Moved the Stone?* (Faber) which shows the opposite. His first chapter is entitled 'The book that refused to be written.'

How can we present the case to someone like the agnostic at the beginning of this study? First we shall look at what the New Testament documents claim happened (it is unnecessary for the agnostic to accept the New Testament as the inspired Word of God at this stage); then we shall consider other theories that have been advanced to meet the facts. Finally we shall look at the meaning of the resurrection for us today.

---

[1]Some have tried to say that there is no need to believe in a literal resurrection; what really matters is that Jesus' spirit lives on in the hearts of the disciples. Such a 'spiritual resurrection' would be inconceivable to the first-century Jew; and if this was all that was intended, why do the documents persist in speaking in literal terms?

1.1 What the documents say

READ the account of Jesus' appearances in Luke, starting at 24:1–53. Then read the parallel accounts in Matthew 28:1–20, Mark 16:1–20 (note that Mark 16:9–20 was probably added later) and John 20 and 21.

Divide your notebook into four columns, listing the events described by each writer, *e.g.*:

Luke	Matthew	Mark	John
24:1–11 Women go to tomb. Stone already rolled away, body gone. Vision of two angels. Women go to the disciples.	28:1–10 The two Marys go to tomb. An angel rolls back the stone and sends them to the disciples. On the way, they see Jesus.	16:1–8 Women go to tomb. They see an angel inside. Sends them to tell others.	20:1–18 Mary alone at the empty tomb. Fetches Peter and the other disciple. After they leave she sees two angels and then she sees Jesus. She goes to tell the other disciples.

You will notice some apparent discrepancies in the Gospel accounts – indeed it would be surprising if they were all exactly the same. Remember each writer gives only a partial picture – you need to combine all the accounts for the full story. Thus Mary Magdalene did not go to the tomb alone (John 20:2 – '*We* don't know where they have put him'), but she went with those women mentioned by the other writers.

You may like to read David Wheaton's article 'The Accounts of the Resurrection' in *The Lion Handbook to the Bible* (Lion, 1973), pp. 529–530, for further information.

Below the four-column table, jot down details of the other appearances mentioned in Acts 1:1–11, 9:1–9 and 1 Corinthians 15:3–10.

Then, using the heading 'Effect on people involved', make a note of the character changes in one of the people involved, Peter. Look up Matthew 14:25–32 and Luke 22:54–62, and compare Acts 4:13–22.

1.2 Objections and alternative theories

Those who do not believe Jesus rose from the dead have suggested various theories, both about the empty tomb and the appearances:

1.2.1 *The body was stolen by the disciples*
This theory had early origins (Matthew 28:11ff.) but how could it explain the psychological changes noted in Peter above, and would people die (and many early Christians did die as martyrs) for something they know to be a lie?

1.2.2 *The body was stolen by the Jewish or Roman authorities*
But if they did steal it, why did they not produce it at the height of the disturbances caused by the disciples' preaching? That indeed would have dealt Christianity a fatal blow. They did not – because they could not.

1.2.3 *The 'swoon theory'*
This theory was originally put forward by Venturini in the eighteenth century with a variation by H. J. Schonfield in *The Passover Plot* (Hutchinson, 1965). It supposes that Jesus, a mere man, did not die on the cross but swooned, revived in the cool of the tomb, found the strength to roll away the stone at its entrance and managed to convince the disciples that he had risen from the dead.

1.2.4 *The appearances were hallucinations*

Medical experts, however, state that hallucinations occur only under certain conditions. In fact, those conditions do not tie up with the resurrection appearances.

■ In your notebook, write down the heading at 1.2 above. Below it summarize the arguments given in 1.2.1 and 1.2.2 above.

■ Write out the heading at 1.2.3. Look up Matthew 27:62–66 and John 19:31–40 and then note down what eye-witness testimony this theory ignores.

■ Using the heading at 1.2.4, write out the following table, and opposite each point suggest a reply from your study of the accounts of the resurrection appearances.

Hallucinations	The appearances
Only occur to those of certain highly strung temperaments.	
Are unique to the persons who experience them. No two people will have exactly the same hallucination.	
Usually concern some eagerly awaited event.	
Are usually restricted to particular times and places.	

The above only gives a summary of the evidence. If you are likely to be involved in a serious debate, you should read the books mentioned at the end of this study.

1.3 Conclusion

The alternative theories do not hold water. The body had gone; people had seen Jesus; his disciples were transformed. No-one can *prove* the resurrection; we have no film showing Jesus actually rise from the dead, yet this is the only adequate explanation we have for the evidence.

Our agnostic still has to take a step of faith to meet Christ – it is not a leap into the dark, however, but an action based on sound facts. For this person the question is no longer an intellectual one – not *'Can* I believe?', but 'Am I *willing* to believe and accept the implications of faith?' For a true story about such a person, read Roger Forster's account of a teacher converted from atheism in *Saturday Night ... Monday Morning* (IVP, 1980), pages 79–81.

> *The problem then concerns, not the adequacy of the evidence, but the openness of the man to admit this fact.*
>
> Clark H. Pinnock, in *Jesus of Nazareth: Saviour and Lord*, ed. by C. F. H. Henry
> (Tyndale Press, 1970), p. 153

PAUSE HERE!

2. WHAT GOD SAYS THROUGH THE RESURRECTION

It is not enough to say that the resurrection took place. As with the death of Christ, the resurrection has profound implications for us today. Through the historical event, God speaks to us ...

2.1 ... about Jesus
We have already looked at passages where Jesus claimed to be divine (John 8:58 in Study Three) and where he demonstrated that he had power over life and death (Luke 7:11–17 in Study Three). Indeed, he foretold that he would rise from the dead (Mark 8:31).

Look up Romans 1:4, preferably in NIV. Write in your own words what Paul is saying here and state why the resurrection is therefore important in evangelism.

The resurrection is also God's statement that what Jesus did on the cross was sufficient for our salvation.

Read Romans 4:23–25 and Ephesians 2:8–9. Then write down an answer to someone who says, 'The only way to get right with God is to live a good life.'

2.2 ... about death

For many, death is the great unmentionable. We dress it up with wreaths of flowers, we try to make it acceptable by the way we describe it – 'passing on', 'being free from suffering'.

Not everyone believes in life after death, however. Bertrand Russell, for instance, said:

'I believe that when I die, I shall rot and nothing of my ego will survive. I am not young, and I love life. But I should scorn to shiver with terror at the thought of annihilation.'[2]

Look up Luke 16:19–31. Now put answers to the following in your notebook:

■ What does Jesus teach about life after death?
■ How do people use the argument in Luke 16:31 today?

Turn to 1 Corinthians 15:51–57 and 2 Corinthians 4:13–14:

■ What does Jesus' resurrection say to the Christian about death?
■ Meditate on your attitude to your own death. What reactions do you have? Are you 'ready' to die?

---

[2]Bertrand Russell, 'What I believe' in *Why I am not a Christian and other essays* (Allen and Unwin, 2nd ed., 1967), p. 49.

2.3. ... about resources available to the Christian

Study Ephesians 1:18–20, especially verses 19 and 20. Write down and pray for any people for whom these verses would be an encouragement.

Note too any situations you are facing where you have not been applying the truth of this passage.

Do the review exercise in your notebook.

For further reading

J. N. D. Anderson, *The Evidence for the Resurrection* (IVP, 1950). Why not buy two or three copies of this excellent booklet (only 16 pages long) to give to friends?
R. T. France, *Jesus the Radical* (IVP, 1989), chapter 11.
Michael Green, *The Day Death Died* (IVP, 1982).
Val Grieve, *Your Verdict* (IVP, 1988).
J. John, *Dead Sure?* (Frameworks, 1989), chapter 9.
Alister McGrath, *Explaining Your Faith* (IVP, 1988), chapter 3.
Frank Morison, *Who Moved the Stone?* (Faber, 1930, 1958).

STUDY FIVE

BORN TO BE KING

> Beyond all question the mystery of godliness is great:
>
> > He appeared in a body,
> > was vindicated by the Spirit,
> was seen by angels,
> > was preached among the nations,
> was believed on in the world,
> > was taken up in glory.   1 Timothy 3:16

God became man; the divine Son became a Jew; the Almighty appeared on earth as a helpless human baby, unable to do more than lie and stare and wriggle and make noises, needing to be fed and changed and taught to talk like any other child. And there was no illusion or deception in this: the babyhood of the Son of God was a reality. The more you think about it, the more staggering it gets. Nothing in fiction is so fantastic as is this truth of the incarnation.

J. I. Packer, *Knowing God* (Hodder, 2nd ed. 1975), p. 73

---

1. Incarnation

Jesus, as we have seen in the last three studies, was

God-in-the-flesh, incarnate (Latin *in carne*, 'in flesh'), fully God and yet fully man. For Paul it was a mystery. How could God's knowledge be limited? How could he truly experience temptation? How could God die? No-one can fully comprehend it since in the incarnation the infinite meets the finite, the other world comes to this world. No analogy can adequately describe it for this event was unique. Yet a biblical understanding of the incarnation is vital if we are to appreciate the greatness of our salvation and the depth of the love God has for us.

1.1 From a human point of view

Mary was an ordinary woman, no different from us, betrothed to Joseph and living in a town some sixty miles from Jerusalem. What can we learn from her?

READ Luke 1:26–56; 2:1–52; and Matthew 1:18 – 2:23.

■ Draw a line down the centre of the next page of your notebook. On the left-hand side, headed 'What actually happened', recap the events and physical and social circumstances surrounding the birth and early years of Jesus. Be brief – this is not a detailed exercise.

What actually happened	What Mary was told

■ On the right-hand side headed 'What Mary was told', list the information about Jesus given to Mary by the angel and others mentioned in the narratives.

■ At various stages, we are given Mary's reaction to what was happening. Below your two-column table, write down what we are told under the heading 'Mary's reaction'. What can we learn from her as we too consider this 'fantastic truth' of the incarnation?

1.2. From God's point of view

The birth narratives emphasize that Jesus was coming as a king who would rescue his people from their sins. Yet he did not come as a remote and aloof potentate; this king deliberately and consciously lowered himself to become one of us; God then exalted him again and he now sits in the place of power with the Father, reigning for eternity.

What did this act of lowering himself involve?

READ Philippians 2:4–8.

In your notebook write answers to the following:

■ What different qualities did Jesus display? (There are at least three.)
■ From your reading of Luke in Study One, write down as many incidents as you can remember where Jesus was serving others.
■ Again from your reading of Luke, note any incidents where Jesus' obedience to the Father was put to the test.

Jesus' relationship with his Father is especially highlighted in the Gospel of John.
■ Look up John 4:34 and write down how Jesus saw this relationship.

47

Heresies

To think of Jesus as fully God and yet fully man is hard for us to grasp, but no harder than it must have been for Mary to react to the facts she was given. Up to AD 500, there was considerable debate as church leaders attempted to formulate their own understanding, which often fell short of the biblical teaching. Set out below are a number of the heresies which were current in the early history of the church.

Ebionism

This regarded Christ not as divine but as a mere man who was qualified at his baptism to be the Messiah by the descent of the Holy Spirit upon him.

Docetism

At the other extreme, docetists denied Christ's true humanity, suggesting that his life on earth was largely an illusion, *i.e.* it was not the divine Christ who hungered and suffered and died.

Gnosticism

Greatly influenced by Greek thought, Gnostics regarded matter as inherently evil. There could be no incarnation since it involved direct contact of spirit with (evil) matter. Some Gnostics believed the Holy Spirit descended on the man Jesus at his baptism but left him before his crucifixion.

Arianism

This theory produced the same effect as Ebionism in that it taught that Jesus was not God in the fullest sense; he had been created by the Father and did not possess eternal self-existence. To counter the heresy, the Council of Nicaea (AD 325) insisted that the words 'of one substance with the Father' should be inserted in the creed commonly accepted by the churches so that it read 'one Lord Jesus Christ . . . very God of very God, begotten not made, being of one substance with the Father'.

Look back to Study Three, on page 34, and make a note of which of today's religions and sects listed there have an Arian view of Jesus.

PAUSE HERE and take a break.

2. APPLICATION

The incarnation was a unique event, and in one sense there is no way we can apply it to ourselves. But if you look at the context of the Philippians 2 passage in 1.2 above, you will see the application, that we are called to have the same attitude to others as the king who lowered himself for the good of his people.

Meditate on the quotation below and consider how far this principle is affecting your life at home, at work, or at college. Write down any changes God may be calling you to make.

> *He did not touch down like a visitor from outer space, or arrive like an alien, bringing his own alien culture with him. He took to himself our humanity, our flesh and blood, our culture. . . . He even bore our sin and died our death. And now he sends us 'into the world' to identify with others as he identified with us . . . to become vulnerable as he did. . . . It is surely one of the most characteristic failures of us Christians . . . that we seldom seem to take seriously this principle of the Incarnation. . . . It comes more natural to us to shout the gospel at people from a distance than to involve ourselves deeply in their lives, to think ourselves into their culture and their problems, and to feel with them in their pains.*
> John Stott, *Christian Mission in the Modern World*
> (Kingsway, 1986), pp. 24–25

3. EXALTATION

After his resurrection, Jesus ascended to heaven and was exalted once more by God the Father as Lord of creation.

READ Ephesians 1:20–23; Hebrews 7:25.

- ■ What is the scope and extent of Jesus' reign?
- ■ What is his work now? In what areas of life does it help to remember Jesus is doing this?

Note The Bible mentions no other person at God's right hand, interceding on our behalf.

Yet this is not the end of the story . . .

4. RETURN AND REIGN

The Bible makes it clear in some two hundred and fifty references that Jesus will one day return to the earth. This second coming, however, will be very different from the first.

How does Scripture answer our questions?[1]

4.1 When will he come again?

Look up Mark 13:32–37 and 2 Peter 3:3–10.

Write down all you can discover about timing and say how you would answer the person who asks about the date of Jesus' return. (Note that scepticism about his return is not new!)

---

[1]It is worth noting that there are areas of controversy about the sequence of events and about interpretation of some of the texts. However, there are no disagreements among biblical Christians about the main teaching as set out in this study.

4.2 What will it be like?

READ Acts 1:11; Matthew 24:30–31; 1 Thessalonians 4:16–17; Revelation 1:7.

Write down what you learn about the manner of his coming. How will it be similar to and how will it differ from the first coming?

4.3 Why will he come again?

Look up the following references and write down why Christ will return; you should discover at least four reasons.

- 1 Corinthians 15:23–28, 51–54
- Matthew 25:31–33; 2 Thessalonians 1:5–10
- Romans 8:18–23
- Revelation 21:1–4; 22:1–5

4.4. How should we react to his coming?

As with all the Bible's teaching it is not enough to know about the particular doctrine. What matters is how we respond to it.

READ 2 Peter 3:11–14 and make a note of how the doctrine should affect our behaviour. Then meditate on the sayings set out below of two great men of God.

> *He who loves the coming of the Lord is not he who affirms that it is far off, nor is it he who says that it is near; but rather he who, whether it be far off or near, awaits it with sincere faith, steadfast hope and fervent love.*
>
> Augustine, as quoted by W. J. Grier in *The Momentous Event*
> (Banner of Truth, 1970), p. 124

> *I do not think that in the last forty years I have lived one conscious hour that was not influenced by the thought of our Lord's return.*
>
> Lord Shaftesbury, as quoted by G. T. Manley in *The Return of Jesus Christ* (IVP, 1960), p. 20

Christianity is unique in that it alone among religions claims that God revealed himself to the human race by becoming a human being and that he rescued us by dying as a human being. From start to finish – from revelation to redemption – it is God who takes the initiative; far from us trying to imagine what God is like and then working our way towards him, God acts in grace and seeks us; and at the end of time, the King will come to take his people to be with him for ever.

Do the review exercise in your notebook.

JESUS AND THE OLD TESTAMENT

> *His recorded words in the Gospels contain more than 40 verbatim quotations, about 60 clear verbal allusions or other references to Old Testament passages and well over 100 other possible allusions, where it is hard to say whether a specific allusion is intended or Jesus' mind was so full of Old Testament words and ideas that he inevitably expressed himself in ways reminiscent of the Old Testament.*
>
> R. T. France, *IBD*, vol. 2, p. 768

For many people the Old Testament is a closed book; a few may have hazy memories of Sunday School lessons about giants and whales and a God of wrath but, apart from its beautiful poetry, they consider it has no relevance.

Jesus' attitude was quite different. His preaching contains references to all the main divisions of the Old Testament – the law, the prophets, the poetic literature – and his teaching and thought patterns, as we have seen from the quotation above, were immersed in these scriptures.

53

1. WHAT CAN WE SAY ABOUT JESUS' ATTITUDE?

1.1 He accepted the truth of Old Testament history

Look up the passages listed below and write answers to the questions that follow:

Luke 17:26–27 (see Genesis 7:1–24)
Luke 10:12 (see Genesis 19:24–28)
Luke 11:29–32 (see Jonah 3:1–6 and 1 Kings 10:1–13)

- What attitude does Jesus take to the incidents referred to?
- What is the significance of his attitude?

Point to ponder
Curiously enough, the narratives that are least acceptable to the so-called 'modern mind' are the very ones that he seemed most fond of choosing for his illustrations.

J. W. Wenham, *Christ and the Bible* (IVP, 2nd ed. 1984), p. 13

1.2 He regarded the Old Testament as inspired by the Holy Spirit

Look up Mark 7:6–13.

- Reading this passage in its context, who does Jesus say was speaking in the Old Testament quotations?

Note For Jesus, human authorship was merely the vehicle through which God spoke. Sometimes Jesus simply says 'It is written' or uses the words 'the Scripture', implying the inspiration of God (*cf.* Luke 7:27; John 7:38). Note, however, that the human authors did not write mechanically; their concerns and often their personalities stand out in the various books and styles of writing.

54

Then, as John Wenham indicates,[1] there is the instance when, for Jesus, 'God' (the Creator) and 'Scripture' are interchangeable. Look up Matthew 19:4–5

1.3 He saw himself as the fulfilment of Old Testament prophecy

It is clear throughout the Gospels that Jesus regarded his whole life and ministry, his death and resurrection, as fulfilling Old Testament prophecy.

Look up Luke 24:25–27 and 44–47, and write out verse 44.

Look again at Luke 4:16–26, which we considered earlier in Study Two. In order to sort out the basic details of the story, take the next page of your notebook and write out simple answers to the questions WHERE? WHEN? WHO? WHAT? WHY?

READ Isaiah 61:1–11, one of the passages referred to by Jesus in Luke 4. This is one of the 'Servant Songs' of Isaiah, seen by the Jews of Jesus' day as prophesying the Saviour or Messiah who would deliver them from Roman occupation. So when Jesus applied it to himself, it was clear he was claiming to be the Messiah.

Go back to the Luke 4 passage and imagine yourself in the shoes of one of the Jewish leaders. How would you have reacted? Write out your answer.

TAKE A BREAK HERE!

[1]*Christ and the Bible* (IVP, 2nd ed. 1984), p. 28.

1.4 He used the Old Testament as authority for his teaching and life

We saw in Study Two how Jesus used the Old Testament to support his teaching. He did this for two reasons: firstly, and most importantly, because for him the Old Testament was God's word; but secondly, he knew too that the teachers of the law (the scribes) and the Pharisees also accepted its authority and claimed it as the basis of their teaching.

By the time Jesus was confronting the scribes and Pharisees, much of the original intent of the Law had been lost. Hundreds of accretions and refinements had been added which sometimes verged on the ridiculous. For example, it was an offence to reap and grind corn 'no greater in bulk than a dried fig' on the sabbath![2] Jesus aimed to do two things: first, to peel away the layers of tradition so people could see what was originally intended and second, to expose the state of mind that led to the law being transgressed.

Look again at Mark 7:9–13.

■ What attitude was Jesus condemning in this passage? Note down your answer.

Note 'Corban' in Mark 7:11 means gift or offering. The tradition had grown up that a person could dedicate to the temple, 'for God's use', money and other possessions that should otherwise have been used to support parents.

For Jesus the Old Testament was still the only guide to right living; his summary of the Law in Matthew 22:36–40 (look up this passage) was a summary of the whole teaching of scriptural ethics. Two points are

[2]Quoted in the Tyndale New Testament Commentary on *Luke* by Leon Morris (IVP, 2nd ed. 1988), p. 135.

56

worth highlighting here: first, Jesus did not *invent* his famous two love commandments – they came straight from the Old Testament. And second, the Old Testament law is not as cold and severe as most law codes today; love was its main ingredient.

Finally, for Jesus, the Old Testament was his authority in the defeat of evil. In Study Two we read in Luke 4:1–13 of the temptation of Jesus. Note that again and again, he counters Satan's accusations by appealing to Scripture. Nor is it simply the quoting of Scripture that defeats the tempter – Satan himself uses Scripture but he twists the text to suit his purpose. Jesus however appeals to the real meaning of the Bible to show where the tempter is in error.

2. OUR OWN ATTITUDE TO THE OLD TESTAMENT

In this study we have looked at the importance Jesus attached to the Old Testament. As Christians who profess to follow Christ, we need to examine very carefully our own attitude to it.

Write down your answers to the following:

■ How much of the Old Testament have you actually read or studied?
■ What kind of authority do you give to its teaching?

> *To Christ the Old Testament was true, authoritative, inspired.*
> *To him the God of the Old Testament was the living God, and the teaching of the Old Testament was the teaching of the living God.*
> *To him, what Scripture said, God said.*
>
> J. W. Wenham, *Christ and the Bible* (IVP, 2nd ed. 1984), p. 37

- Remembering that you have already been chal-
  lenged about this in Study Two (see p. 23), is there
  any action you still have to take?

Do the review exercise in your notebook.

For further reading

Cyril Bridgland and Francis Foulkes, *Pocket Guide to
the Bible* (IVP, 1988), pp. 15–37.
Edmund P. Clowney, *The Unfolding Mystery* (IVP,
1990).

JESUS' TEACHING (1) GOD AND US

'No-one ever spoke the way this man does,' the guards declared.   John 7:46

The crowds were amazed at his teaching, because he taught as one who had authority, and not as their teachers of the law.   Matthew 7:28–29

Wherever Jesus went, people were struck by his teaching. It was not just the methods he used – vivid parables drawn from everyday life, commonplace incidents used as a natural springboard for making a particular point – but more than that, people instinctively knew that here was someone whose words could not be ignored. The same holds true today – and as we saw in Study Three, if Jesus is God, then what he says is final and authoritative and we must accept it whether or not we like it or find it convenient or even fully comprehend it.

In his teaching, Jesus answers three basic questions, the subject of this study.

1. WHAT IS GOD LIKE?

We saw in Study Three that Jesus shocked the Jewish

authorities by declaring that God was his Father. But his teaching included a truth that was in reality even more shocking: those who were restored to a right relationship with God were also to refer to him as Abba; God, in fact, was not only Jesus' Father but their Father too. Now Jesus made it clear that this relationship with the Father was a distinct and exclusive one (*cf.* John 1:12–13) and that we can call God Father only when we have the Spirit of Christ in us; there is no question of God being the Father of all human beings. Christians are, in fact, *adopted* into God's family; they are his children neither by right, nor in substance, as Jesus is.

What does Jesus teach about God's fatherhood?

■ First, write down your picture of an ideal father – his role; his character; how he behaves towards his children.

■ Now, build up a picture of the heavenly Father from the following and jot it down in your notebook; make a note of the ways in which our heavenly Father is infinitely better than any human father could ever be.
  Matthew 6:8
  Matthew 10:29–31
  Luke 15:11–32

■ Christ's revelation also included the corollary fact that if God is our Father, then Jesus is our brother (Luke 8:19–21), and we are his brothers or sisters. What does it mean to you to see Jesus in this way? Write down your answer.

■ Now read Romans 8:14–17, where Paul enlarges on the Christian position. Write down the privileges we enjoy as God's children. Make a note of what is also an inevitable consequence of this relationship. (See also point 3.4 in Study Eight.)

2. WHO AM I?

Jesus taught both by precept and by example that each individual is precious and of great worth.

2.1 All are made in God's image – they are of great value

Look up Matthew 25:31–46 and write answers to the following:

■ Who does Jesus call his brothers (and, by implication, sisters)?
■ Why is he able to call them this? (See Study Two, section 1 – though this is in a different sense from that discussed in 1.3 above.)

Note For Jesus, the sign that confirms a person has accepted him as Saviour is when that person displays the love that Christ had for other people.

2.2. All are equal in God's eyes – there are no barriers

Make a list of the barriers that divide people from each other today.

Now look up briefly the incidents in Luke 7:36–50 and John 4:1–30, and list:

■ the different kinds of people involved
■ the barriers that separated them from others

The criticisms levelled at Jesus indicate his attitude to social misfits (Luke 19:7), but he stated clearly that it was the 'lost' like them whom he had come to save (Luke 19:10).

■ What sort of people do you number among your friends?
■ Who do you spend time with? People with the same interests and outlook as you?
■ Does your attitude match that of Jesus – or are

there changes you are going to make after this study?

Make a note of your answers.

We need to beware of worldly attitudes creeping into our thinking. Some Christians seem to despise the poor, ignoring them completely as did the rich man in Luke 16:19ff., or else being satisfied by a donation to charity without actually coming into contact with the needy. To live where they live, to eat where they eat, is never considered.

Other Christians seem to despise the rich and speak of them with scorn. Jesus gives us no grounds for doing this; on the contrary, the rich are to be treated with compassion as it is so hard for them to enter heaven (Luke 18:24–27).

■ How Christ-like is your attitude to the poor?
■ How Christ-like is your attitude to the rich?

Be honest with yourself as you write down your answers.

2.3 All are sinful in God's eyes – there are no excuses

Look up Mark 7:14–23 and write down answers to the following:

■ What different causes are given today for evil behaviour?
■ What source does Jesus give for evil? What is he thereby implying?
■ In what way does Jesus' analysis lend more dignity to humanity?

Note There is one kind of person Jesus cannot help.

READ Luke 18:9–14. Who is it?

TAKE A BREAK HERE.

3. WHAT IS OUR DESTINY?

Jesus gives only two alternatives:

READ John 14:1–3; Matthew 25:45–46.

Write in your own words what these verses teach.

Some who have never studied closely Jesus' message speak warmly of his ethical teaching and contrast it unfavourably with the 'God of wrath' of the Old Testament. Yet perhaps the most vivid revelation we have of the final destiny of the unsaved has come from the lips of Jesus. In at least two thirds of Luke's Gospel there is some statement, direct or implied, about God's judgment – the fact of judgment is, therefore, unavoidable. (For example, *cf.* Luke 10:14; 11:30–31; 12:4–5.)

Make a note of how you would answer the person who quotes 1 Timothy 2:3–4 and says that all people will be saved in the end. (This view is widespread and is known as universalism.)

Do the review exercise in your notebook.

STUDY EIGHT

JESUS' TEACHING (2) THE KINGDOM

But he said, 'I must preach the good news of the kingdom of God to the other towns also, because that is why I was sent.'   Luke 4:43

As we went through Luke in Study One, we saw that the kingdom of God is a theme to which Jesus keeps returning.

In Study Three we considered the Jewish expectation of a Messiah who would establish God's kingdom on earth and we looked briefly at the nature of Jesus' kingship in Study Five. Now we shall study more closely this central theme of Jesus' teaching.

1. THE NATURE OF THE KINGDOM

In your notebook, write answers to the following:

Look up John 18:36; Luke 17:20–21 (RSV).

◼ What misconceptions does Jesus correct and what does he teach instead about the nature of the kingdom?

READ Luke 7:18–23; 11:14–20.

◼ In what ways does the establishment of the kingdom

appear and what does this teach about the scope of the King's rule?

READ Matthew 13:24–33.

■ Jesus uses three parables here when speaking of the kingdom. What lessons do they have for us?

Look up Luke 21:25–31 and 34–36.

■ If the kingdom is already here, what is Jesus teaching in these verses?

As we have seen, the kingdom of God has come – people are healed, the good news is preached, demons are cast out. Yet the kingdom is in many ways hidden; like a small seed, or a piece of yeast, it is working away, unseen, its effects gradually pervading the world. The King has arrived – but as a servant.

One day, however, at the end of present world-history, the King is to come again (see Study Five) for the final harvest, and then the kingdom will no longer be provisional or its effects partly hidden – then the kingdom will come in its full and final force.

However much the kingdom invades world-history with its blessing and deliverance, however much it presents itself as a saving power against the tyranny of gods and forces inimical to mankind, it is only through a final and universal crisis that the kingdom, as a visible and all-conquering reign of peace and salvation, will bring to full fruition the new heaven and the new earth.

H. N. Ridderbos, article on 'Kingdom of God', in *IBD*, vol. 2, p. 855

---

2. ENTRY TO THE KINGDOM

Some people today assume that entry to the kingdom is achieved through various means: living a good life, attending church or being baptized or confirmed. Jesus taught otherwise.

READ John 3:1–16.

Write down your answers in your notebook:

■ Who was Nicodemus? ·
■ What was his unspoken question?
■ What was his misunderstanding (John 3:4)?
■ How does a person enter the kingdom (John 3:3, 15–16)? Try to describe what is necessary in your own words.

Now write out and memorize John 1:12, which highlights these truths.

TAKE A BREAK HERE.

3. LIFE IN THE KINGDOM

Nicodemus was a religious leader and yet he came to realize that despite all his Jewish upbringing he had not yet found the way to eternal life. Then, as now, much of what God had revealed of himself through the Old Testament had been virtually lost from view by the encrustation of tradition and a system of rules and regulations that required a whole body of teachers to interpret them.

Jesus, of course, did more than remind people of the Old Testament revelation; he himself was God's new and final revelation, the fulfilment of all to which the Old Testament pointed.

What would life in the kingdom involve? It would mean:

3.1 The rejection of religious formalism

Throughout his earthly life, Jesus was engaged in controversy with the religious rulers of his day, who had

67

become trapped in their traditional ways. Jesus criticized them in three areas:

3.1.1 *Legalism*

READ Luke 6:1–11. (The Pharisees had regulations which forbade reaping, threshing and preparing food on the Sabbath. They also forbade healing on the Sabbath unless there was danger to life.)

■ What was God's original intention in each case?
■ Where had the Pharisees gone wrong?

3.1.2 *Hypocrisy*

READ Matthew 6:1–6.

■ What practices was Jesus condemning here?

3.1.3 *Intellectualism*

READ John 5:39–40.

■ What was the underlying problem?

Note Jesus made it clear that the problem was with the will, not in the realm of understanding.

It is very tempting for us to want to apply these truths directly to the modern situation and to see all sorts of parallels in different church fellowships, forgetting that Jesus himself continued to worship in the formal setting of the synagogue. We must take most seriously Jesus' warning against judging others before we judge ourselves (Matthew 7:1–5).

■ Examine yourself: are you in danger of falling into any of these traps, and if so which ones?

3.2 A right attitude to Jesus

READ Luke 5:1–11.

- Who takes the initiative throughout?
- What different stages of understanding does Peter go through?

Notice Peter's first reaction when he is spiritually awakened, and *cf.* Isaiah 6:1–5.

As we saw in Study Four, life for Peter would never be the same again after he met Jesus, and that leads us to another element of life in the kingdom.

3.3 **A willingness to serve**

Jesus himself was the pattern for us. Look back to Study Five and your answer to the question on Philippians 2:4–8 in section 1.2.

READ Luke 17:7–10.

- Write down what is involved in being a servant in the kingdom of God.
- In what areas are you serving the Master?
- How do you think he rates your service?

3.4 **Counting and accepting the cost**

READ Luke 9:23–26.

- Specify what you may be called on to do in serving Christ and assess your willingness to do this.
- What is it that makes it possible for us to endure the cost?
- What does taking up your cross daily involve in your life? (Be very specific.)

∎ ∎ ∎

These four areas are a necessary part of life in the kingdom. Yet Jesus does not ask us to reject hypocrisy, and to give him service that will cost us physically and emotionally, without also giving us the means to obey him. Everyone who has received Christ has the Spirit of Christ, the Holy Spirit, in them and so can enjoy Christ's power to stand out, Christ's power to serve, Christ's power to suffer.

As Jesus made clear, the kingdom of God arrived with him. He reigns in the life of each Christian and, one day, his rule will extend to all people and all creation, whether or not they have voluntarily submitted to him. There is as we have seen a present fulfilment of the kingdom – but there is also a future aspect which should encourage us when we are tempted to despair at the state of the world.

Do the review exercise in your notebook.

For further reading

R. T. France, *Jesus the Radical* (IVP, 1989), chapter 8.

THE CROSS

For I resolved to know nothing while I was with you except Jesus Christ and him crucified.

1 Corinthians 2:2

... but we preach Christ crucified: a stumbling-block to Jews and foolishness to Gentiles.

1 Corinthians 1:23

The cross has long been the heart and the symbol of the Christian faith, yet people are puzzled as to why this should be. Many people both before and since have suffered just as much physical torture at the hands of their killers. Was it the tragic end to an idealist's dream? Or the supreme example of the noble way to die? In this study we shall consider the true significance of the cross and how it applies to our daily lives.

1. THE DEATH OF GOD

1.1 What actually happened

Most of us assume we know the principal events surrounding Jesus' death, yet it is easy to miss important details.

71

Draw up a chart in your notebook using the following headings:

Events	What Jesus said	Unusual occurrences

READ Luke 22:39 – 23:56.

Fill in the chart, leaving gaps between each entry.

READ Matthew 27:32–61 and John 19:16–37.

Complete the chart, filling in the gaps where appropriate.

Note The words 'It is finished' (John 19:30) translate the Greek *tetelestai* meaning 'it is paid' (as on a receipt, for example).

1.2. Inside story

It is obviously vital to see how the Son of God viewed his own death.

Look up Luke 9:20–22.

Far from his death representing dashed hopes to a young idealist, it is clear that in Jesus' mind he came expressly to die.

Write out Mark 10:45 and memorize it.

READ Matthew 26:26–29.

Try to imagine you were present as a disciple, knowing nothing of the later teaching about the cross.

■ With what did Jesus link his death?

72

■ Since this meal took place during the Passover celebrations, what parallels might have run through your mind? (Exodus 12:1–14 will give you the origin of the Festival if you are not familiar with it.)

For Jesus, then, his death (and his resurrection) were a necessity; to achieve his mission would involve identifying with sinners and almost unbearable suffering, yet he went to his death voluntarily, not as some puppet strung along by events.

PAUSE FOR A BREAK.

2. SIGNIFICANCE

In the Bible, Jesus is seen as . . .

2.1 Our sacrifice

The Bible teaches that the wages or penalty of sin is death, not just physical death, but spiritual death which leaves a person insensitive to God and cut off from him. To satisfy the demands of justice, God must punish sin and the sinner must die.

Is there a way in which God can punish sin without producing an irreversible separation between himself and the whole of humanity? Can he show love without condoning sin? The answer lies in the sacrificial death of God's Son, a solution foreshadowed by Old Testament sacrifice.

> *Death is the word which sums up the whole liability of man in relation to sin, and therefore, when Christ came to give Himself for our sins, He did it by dying.*
>
> James Denney, *The Death of Christ* (Tyndale Press, 1951), p. 76

The books of Leviticus (in the Old Testament) and Hebrews (in the New Testament) spell out the meaning of sacrifice and help us understand how the coming of Christ brought a whole new dimension to the concept.

READ Hebrews 9:6–14, 22–28.

■ List, in your notebook, the ways in which Christ as High Priest and as sacrifice makes perfect what was foreshadowed in the Old Testament system.

■ Jesus saw his death as a necessity. Why? Was there no other way of saving humanity?

■ What is meant by the phrase 'once for all' in Hebrews 9:12, 26?

■ What then is the basis for God's forgiveness of people in Old Testament times?

■ Jot down what you would say to the adherents of any religion which claimed to be led by 'today's Messiah'.

Objections

■ *The blood of Christ*   Some people dislike the idea of being 'blood-bought' or hymns which speak of fountains 'filled with blood'. It is important to note that to speak in this way of blood is to use spiritual language; that, in Scripture, bloodshed represents life poured out (Leviticus 17:11) and that to change the metaphor means that the real meaning is lost.

■ *Propitiation*   This means the removal of wrath by the offering of a gift and is used in the older versions of the Bible to describe Jesus' sacrifice, in Romans 3:25. Some who object to the idea of a wrathful God prefer to use 'expiation' (RSV, meaning 'blotting out') or 'a sacrifice of atonement' (NIV). Yet it is perfectly biblical to talk of the wrath of God – not an uncontrolled or impulsive rage, but the relentless anger of a just God against all that is evil. Note too that it is *God* who initiates the means of propitiation (Romans 3:25). Talk, therefore, of a God who vents uncontrolled rage against helpless sinners is totally wrong.

2.2 Our substitute and representative

READ Leviticus 16:20–22; 1 Peter 2:24.

We saw in Study Three that Jesus was sinless. So what happened on the cross?

■ Look back to the chart you drew at the beginning of this study. Think how Jesus' words on the cross and the unusual occurrences tie in with what we have learned and write down your thoughts.

Many have been confused by the terms 'representative' and 'substitute'. Both are important. One helpful distinction is to say that for the unbeliever, Christ is his *substitute* since 'Christ does not commit sin, and we do not make atonement'.[1] Christ has done something on the cross that no human being could ever do.

When a person becomes a Christian, however, he realizes that what Jesus has done must be reproduced in his own life. He accepts, therefore, that when Jesus died, he was dying as his *representative* and he is 'baptized into' the death of Christ as if he himself had died on the cross with Jesus. His new life then begins. The death of Jesus counts as the death of those he represents, hence his need to be fully human as he, the great High Priest, represents us before God.

Write down answers to the following:

■ Was it not unjust of God to allow an innocent third party to suffer for the sins of humanity?
■ Why was it vital to the effectiveness of Christ's death that our sinbearer should be fully God and yet fully human?

[1]James Denney, *The Death of Christ* (Tyndale Press, 1951), p. 133.

2.3 Our redeemer

READ Leviticus 25:47–55; John 8:31–36. The picture is that of slavery.

■ To what is man enslaved? How does this show itself in your life?

■ What then is the cross saying, and how can you apply this to yourself?

Make a note of your answers.

Note Theologians tend to use the word 'atonement' to describe what Jesus did on the cross. It derives from a medieval Latin word meaning 'a making at one' of those who are estranged.

3. THE CROSS TODAY

3.1 The cross and the unbeliever

■ How does Jesus' death satisfy both the justice and the love of God? Note your answer in the notebook. (Look back at your answers in section 2.1.)

■ Write down how you would explain Jesus as our sacrifice and Jesus as our redeemer to a friend. What illustrations or analogies would you use?

3.2 The cross in the life of the Christian

Two truths central to teaching about the cross are vital to our sense of assurance.

3.2.1 *Justification*

The Bible teaches that when a person accepts Christ by faith as his Saviour, he is then accounted righteous in God's eyes for all time, not because of anything worthy in him but because of the saving work of Christ who has paid sin's fixed penalty, death, on his behalf.

God accounts sinners righteous 'not because he accounts them to have kept his law personally (which would be a false judgment), but because he accounts them to be "in" the One who kept God's law representatively (which is a true judgment)'.[2]

A person is thus said to be justified. Justification is a once-for-all declaration that need never be repeated. It should not be confused with forgiveness.

3.2.2 *Forgiveness*
Scripture makes it clear that we need to ask for God's forgiveness each time we sin (1 John 1:9). But having to go on asking for forgiveness does not mean we must go on asking to be justified; that, as we have said, is a once-for-all event. Finding ourselves falling time and again into the same sin does not affect our eternal security, though it does affect our moment-by-moment relationship with God.

The following table from *In Understanding Be Men*[3] shows the contrast between forgiveness and justification:

Forgiveness	*Justification*
An act, followed by a succession of such acts.	An act, followed by an attitude.
Repeated throughout life.	Complete and never repeated.
Negative, removing condemnation.	Positive, the bestowal of a proper standing before God.
Does not of itself alter formal status.	A reinstatement.

[2] J. I. Packer, *IBD*, vol. 2, p. 844.
[3] T. C. Hammond, *In Understanding Be Men*, ed. by D. F. Wright (Tyndale Press, 6th ed. 1968), p. 143.

Meditate on the following testimony, which shows how one man was affected when he saw the distinction between these two truths.

I dragged my feet through life beneath a burden of guilt. . . . How could I confess the same sin for the hundredth time? Where was my sincerity? . . . Light began to break over me when I realized in the depths of my spirit that I was forgiven, cleansed, accepted, justified because of what Christ had done for me *and not because of the depth of my yieldedness. I had preached this gospel to non-Christians for twenty-five years but had never tasted its full sweetness. . . . Suddenly the relief of knowing that I was forgiven and loved lifted the load off my spirit. . . . To my astonishment I discovered that I wanted to live a holy life far more than I wanted to sin. Forgiveness freed me to do what I wanted most.*

John White, *The Fight* (IVP, 1977), pp. 185–186

Do the review exercise in your notebook.

For further reading

Peter Cotterell, *This is Christianity* (IVP, 1985), chapter 3.
R. T. France, *Jesus the Radical* (IVP, 1989), chapter 10.
Val Grieve, *The Trial of Jesus* (IVP/STL, 1990).
J. John, *Dead Sure?* (Frameworks, 1989), chapters 7 and 8.
Alister McGrath, *Explaining Your Faith* (IVP, 1988), chapter 4.
John Stott, *The Cross of Christ* (IVP, 1986). A fairly demanding read, and already a classic.

JESUS – OUR GOAL

(Since this is the last of the ten studies, try to set aside an evening or a morning to complete it and to leave adequate time for review, prayer and meditation.)

> *You diligently study the Scriptures because you think that by them you possess eternal life. These are the Scriptures that testify about me, yet you refuse to come to me to have life.*   John 5:39–40

In this book, we have been studying the Scriptures and we have seen how they testify about Jesus. Yet for us, as for the Pharisees to whom Jesus originally spoke them, the words quoted above are potentially among the most chilling in all the Bible. As we saw in Study Eight, the Pharisees' diligent and earnest search of Scripture ended in them completely missing the point; it is possible also for us to complete a series of studies on Jesus, indeed to write such a series, and equally to miss the point.

If we are Christians, we have come to Jesus in a way the Pharisees had not; we have opened our lives to Christ and received him. Yet many Christians know from experience the dangers of amassing a great fund of knowledge *about* Christ which, if not applied and linked to personal dealings *with* him, leaves us dry and spiritually hungry. It is for this reason that each study has contained questions to help us apply what we have learned of Jesus, to allow God to speak to us personally.

■ ■ ■

Now we are to look at just part of what Jesus said to his disciples before he died. He had only a short time left. It is interesting to see then that the priority uppermost in his mind was the same as in the conversation with the Pharisees in John 5:39–40; for what Jesus most wanted his disciples to remember was the absolute necessity of coming to him and remaining in him.

READ John 15:1–17.

1. THE VINE – A PICTURE OF OUR RELATIONSHIP WITH JESUS

Consider the image of the vine in John 15:1, 3–5, and write answers to the following in your notebook:

■ Why is a vine grown?
■ What is the relationship between the main plant and the branches?
■ What different kinds of branches are there?
■ When do they bear fruit?
■ In what ways does this image speak of the relationship between Christ and the Christian?

1.1. The Christian's life depends on union with Christ (John 15:5)

At the moment of becoming Christians, we are united with Christ; united to the extent that in God's eyes we share in Christ's death and rise to a new life.

Write out Romans 6:3–4; Galatians 2:20.

As the sap from the main plant courses through the branches and gives them life and vitality, so the life of Jesus courses through new Christians bringing them to life, and empowering them to live in the way God intended.

1.2 The Christian's effectiveness depends on remaining united with Christ (John 15:4, 9–10)

Write answers to the following:

■ What kind of fruit is God looking for? Look up Galatians 5:22–23.
■ What do you think Jesus means by 'remaining' or 'abiding' (RSV)?
■ What resources has God given us by which we may remain united with Christ?

Meditate on John 15:16a.

■ How should this truth affect your relationship to Christ and your view of Christian service?

READ John 15:2a and 6.

These words do not mean that a person who is a Christian can subsequently be cut off from God. Once a person has been justified (see 3.2.1 in Study Nine), that person's eternal destiny is decided for ever. These verses, therefore, are talking about those who *appear* to be Christians, and who flourish for a time, but who later fall away since in fact they never did belong to Christ. As R. V. G. Tasker says,[1] Judas Iscariot is 'the outstanding example' of this.

[1]Tyndale New Testament Commentary on *John* (IVP, 1960), p. 175.

81

1.3 Increased effectiveness depends on careful pruning (John 15:2–3)

■ What will be your experience if you are a fruitful Christian (15:2)?

■ What among other means does God use to prune us (15:3)? Make a note of any experience you can remember of this.

■ What might God still want to prune in your life? Jot down any areas where you sense there is pruning to be done. (Remember that pruning does not only involve removal of dead wood – it can involve cutting away shoots that are good in themselves but which are in the wrong place and using up precious sap.)

1.4. Specific obedience leads to specific results

If all that we have just studied is painful to contemplate, consider what results Jesus expects. He mentions three. Write them down.

■ John 15:5 and 8; *cf.* Hebrews 12:11
■ John 15:7 and 16b
■ John 15:11

If you are not experiencing these in your life, try to analyse why, and write down what action you need to take.

Note There are conditions in John 15:7 and 16b that are attached to our prayers being answered according to our requests. 'Prayer is not a convenient device for imposing our will upon God, or bending his will to ours, but the prescribed way of subordinating our will to his.'[2]

[2]John Stott, Tyndale Commentary on *The Letters of John* (IVP, 2nd ed. 1988), p. 188.

2. Fellow Christians – another priority

If maintaining our relationship with him was uppermost in Jesus' mind before he died, our relationship with other Christians was a high priority too. This is clear from one of his final prayers.

READ John 17:11, 20–23, slowly and thoughtfully.

Now go back to John 15. In your notebook, write answers to the following questions:

■ In what terms does Jesus speak of loving fellow (John 15:12a, 17)?
■ How does this differ from the way people normally think of love?

Some might argue that it is hypocritical to love only because you are told to.

■ How would you answer this?
■ What is the standard of love Jesus requires (John 15:12b–13)?
■ Are you obeying this command of Jesus or are you conscious that there are Christians whom you do not love because of a 'personality conflict' or some past hurt they have caused you?
■ What does this say of your love for Jesus (15:10)?
■ What action do you intend to take?

3. FRIENDSHIP WITH JESUS – OUR INCREDIBLE PRIVILEGE

Towards the end of this passage, Jesus, for the first time, speaks of his disciples as 'friends'.

■ Write down what friendship means for you. What does it involve?
■ Think of the person you consider your best friend. What is it that you particularly value about this relationship?

Now look at what Christ says.

■ What does friendship involve for Jesus (John 15:15)? Make a note of your answer.

In God's eyes, this has always been so . . .

READ Psalm 25:14, and Genesis 18:17–19 (*cf.* 2 Chronicles 20:7).

■ Write down what friendship involves for a disciple (John 15:14; *cf.* Psalm 25:14a).

Take a few minutes to consider the fact that Jesus intends us to be his friends.

■ What kind of a friendship do you have with him?
■ What do you give to that friendship?

Note your thoughts in your notebook.

PAUSE FOR A BREAK.

4. REVIEW

Go back over your notebook and, taking one study at a time, skim over what you wrote for the whole of that study (not just the review exercise at the end), then write down answers to the following:

- ■ What were the main two or three points I learned?
- ■ What action did I take or have I still to take?
- ■ How has this study affected my attitude to and relationship with Christ?

When you have completed the final review for all ten studies, take as long as you can to pray, to worship Jesus and to let his personality and love surround you. Make sure you really have dealings with him – don't be satisfied with an academic exercise.

■ ■ ■

This man, this God wants to be your friend. He knows what it is to live in our world, to suffer the everyday grind, the ups and downs of human existence, and he knows too the deep pain of tragedy. But he has done so much more than identify with human experience; he has conquered every kind of evil that humanity can devise and worse; he has even conquered the last enemy, death. One day all men and women and all of creation will be forced to acknowledge his authority and his power.

He calls you now to be his friend – on his terms. His call will involve you in adventure, in unspeakable joy, in deep fulfilment; it will also involve you in pain, in misunderstanding, in disappointment.

Are you willing to be done with a discipleship that is at best grudging and unsatisfying, and exchange it for a total commitment to one who can use every ounce of potential in you for his glory and for the service of mankind? Will you submit to Jesus as your master? Will you look to him as your guide? Will you have him as your friend?

The Fight

JOHN WHITE

John White has written this book because he wants you to understand clearly what the Christian life is all about. He wants you to learn in the depths of your being that the eternal God loves you and plans only your highest good – more trust in him, more likeness to him.

But his love will bring pain as intense as your joy. For the Christian life is a fight....

"Reading *The Fight* is to inhale great draughts of fresh air into one's Christian life... This is the kind of book every 20th Century Christian should have on his book shelf."

Christian Weekly Newspapers

230 pages   Pocketbook

Inter-Varsity Press

Jesus the Radical
A portrait of the man they crucified

R. T. FRANCE

Some sought his death. Others left everything to
follow him. Who *was* this Jesus, this carpenter
turned wandering teacher? Why did he provoke
such extreme reactions? And why does he still
do so today, two thousand years after his death?

Jesus the Radical highlights the impact of Jesus
against the backdrop of life in first-century
Judea, with its customs, its messianic hopes, its
multi-faceted Judaism and its Roman overlords.
Here are many fascinating insights into the story
you thought you knew.

'Sensitive and compelling . . . It confronts the
reader with Jesus and lets him decide what
responses to make.' *Christianity Today*

224 pages   *Pocketbook*

Inter-Varsity Press

Dead Sure?
about yourself, life, faith
J. JOHN

Team up a popular and experienced evangelist with a highly talented, full-colour illustrator and make the resulting book available at a truly affordable price. Then you have an effective and lively explanation of Christianity for today's young adult.

Dead Sure? combines an author who clearly understands his audience and a format that draws the reader in and 'speaks' alongside the text.

96 pages   *Large paperback*

FRAMEWORKS

Explaining Your Faith
(without losing your friends)
ALISTER McGRATH

You want to tell your non-Christian friends how exciting and relevant Christianity is. But what do you say?

Christian faith looks very different from the outside looking in! How can you explain it so that it makes sense to your friends?

Alister McGrath's book provides a straightforward, readable and intelligible account of what Christians believe – and why they believe it. He takes key topics that often come up in discussions, and shows how to explain them clearly.

112 pages   *Pocketbook*

Inter-Varsity Press